MOUNT KINABALU

BORNEO'S MAGIC MOUNTAIN

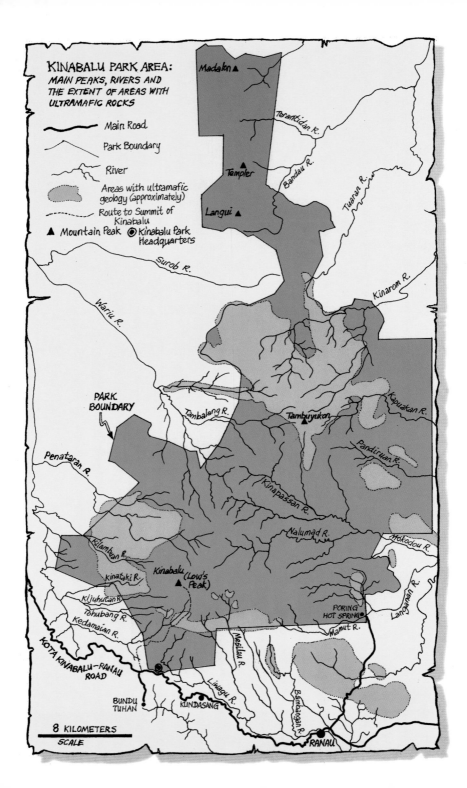

KINABALU PARK AREA:
MAIN PEAKS, RIVERS AND
THE EXTENT OF AREAS WITH
ULTRAMAFIC ROCKS

——— Main Road

Park Boundary

River

Areas with ultramafic
geology (approximately)

Route to Summit of
Kinabalu

▲ Mountain Peak ⊙ Kinabalu Park
Headquarters

Madalon ▲

Templer ▲

Langui ▲

Terantidan R.

Bandau R.

Tuaran R.

Surob R.

Kinarom R.

Wariu R.

PARK
BOUNDARY

Tambalang R.

Tambuyukon ▲

Kapuakan R.

Penataran R.

Pandiruan R.

Kinapassan R.

Nalumad R.

Mokodou R.

Kilambun R.

Kinataki R.

Kinabalu
▲ (Low's
Peak)

Langaran R.

Kijuhutan R.

Tohubang R.

Kedamaian R.

PORING
HOT SPRING ⊙

Mamut R.

KOTA KINABALU–RANAU
ROAD

Mesilau R.

Linagu R.

Bambangan R.

BUNDU
TUHAN ●

KUNDASANG ●

RANAU ●

8 KILOMETERS
SCALE

MOUNT KINABALU
BORNEO'S MAGIC MOUNTAIN

*an introduction to the natural history of
one of the world's great natural monuments*

K.M. Wong and C.L. Chan

Natural History Publications
Kota Kinabalu

1997

Published by

Natural History Publications (Borneo) Sdn. Bhd.,
A913, 9th Floor, Wisma Merdeka,
P.O. Box 13908,
88846 Kota Kinabalu, Sabah, Malaysia

First published 1997

MOUNT KINABALU—Borneo's Magic Mountain
*an introduction to the natural history of one of
the world's great natural monuments*
by K.M. Wong and C.L. Chan

Cover photograph by Tommy Chang
Back cover photograph by C.L. Chan

Perpustakaan Negara Malaysia Cataloguing-in-Publication Data

Wong, K.M. (Khoon Meng)
        Mount Kinabalu: Borneo's magic mountain: an introduction
        to the natural history of one of the world's great natural
        monuments / K.M. Wong and C.L. Chan.
        Bibliography : p. 93
        ISBN 983-812-014-6
        1. Gunung Kinabalu (Sabah). 2. Natural monuments—Sabah.
        3. Nature conservation—Sabah. I. Chan, C.L. (Chew Lun).
        II. Title.
        508.359521

Printed in Malaysia.

CONTENTS

v

Foreword

Kinabalu has attracted so much attention from climbers, naturalists, conservationists and tourists in general that it has become an icon of tropical nature in the Far East. Scientifically, too, Kinabalu has held the fascination of many scholars from far and near, and even more has been written about the mountain and its biota in journals and specialist works in recent years.

Yet much of this information has not been easily accessible to most of Kinabalu's visitors. While studies on the natural environment and biological diversity of this wonderful mountain are far from complete—due to the sheer difficulty in tackling the many parts of its difficult terrain and the enormous array of life forms—we have now come to appreciate the salient aspects of its physical environment and their influence on biological evolution.

Here in this short account is explained why Kinabalu should be so interesting, in historical, environmental and biological terms. With this, it is hoped that visitors will take with them not just enjoyable memories of Kinabalu, but also an understanding of how its ecosystems are special and how this great mountain has become a true symbol of natural history and conservation.

Datuk Lamri Ali
Director,
Sabah Parks

P.K. Loi

OF MOUNTAINS AND PEAKS
An Introduction to Kinabalu

Mount Kinabalu, rising to 4101 m, has not only the distinction of being the highest peak between the Himalayas and Irian Jaya (New Guinea), but also its remarkable biological diversity has not ceased to captivate scientists the world over. Protected within the Kinabalu Park of some 753.7 sq. km, it totally dominates an area which includes a fascinating range of vegetation types and habitats.

Kinabalu is now probably one of the most accessible high mountains to visitors because of its location only some 90 km by good road from Sabah's modern state capital of Kota Kinabalu. It was, however, a very different situation described by Hugh Low (who first climbed Kinabalu in 1851) and Spenser St. John (who climbed it twice in 1862, with Low). They encountered extraordinary logistical problems travelling by sea from Labuan to Tuaran or Abai on the coast, and on foot through difficult terrain. However, the first recorded climb to the highest point, now called Low's Peak, was made by the great zoologist John Whitehead in 1888.

Yet today Kinabalu remains one of the true wild places of the tropics because its immense proportions and rugged landscape have still not been thoroughly explored, in spite of having attracted scientific attention since the middle of the 19th century. The Kinabalu Park was established in 1964, before the great waves of tourism, and the careful conservation approach of restricting general visitation to only some parts and routes (which still offer a great deal to see and experience) has kept disturbance by human activities to a minimum. Whereas in 1965 there were only 879 recorded visits (including 700 by climbers of Kinabalu itself) to the Park,

(Opposite) The silhouette of Kinabalu dominates the skyline on the Tuaran plains, from where early expeditions approached the mountain.

F.S.P. Liew

(Above) Low's Peak (4101 m), Kinabalu's highest.
Climbers return from a pre-dawn ascent that is usual nowadays for observing the first moments of sunrise over Borneo.

K.M. Wong

Glacial super-highway.
An open, inclined passage near St. John's Peak, "bulldozed" by huge moving ice-sheets nearly 100,000 years ago.

Kinabalu emerges in the hues of dawn, a solitary gigantic feature that is Borneo's most famous landmark.

in 1975 this increased nearly tenfold to 7086 (with 2126 climbers), and nearly another twenty years later in 1994 this had swelled to 200,907 (with 29,574 climbers). The usual climber's route to the summit from Park Headquarters is 8.5 km, accomplished by most people over two days, or in just a few hours if one were an extremely fit participant of the annual "Climbathon", an event attracting competitors from different countries.

K.M. Wong

With the clouds below, the landscape around South Peak (3933 m) is a bizarre rock-desert. Superficial parts of the huge granitic body that formed the mountain break off as slabs, as a result of alternate high and low temperatures, a process called exfoliation. The generally smooth slopes were the path of a south- and westward-flowing glacier during cooler episodes of the earth's climate. Here, near the very top, only small herbs and dwarf shrubs persist, clinging onto crevices and hollows.

Tengku D.Z. Adlin

An unusual view of the Donkey's Ears, one of Kinabalu's most characteristic summit features, viewed from Low's Gully.

The "Ears", silhouetted against the sky towards the left, are the remnants of a U-shaped hanging valley that once contained a glacier and now brought to ruin by weathering and collapse.

For centuries before the arrival of Low and St. John, Kinabalu had already asserted its awesome and important role in the cultures of the indigenous peoples who lived in the shadow of this great mountain. In the folklore and traditional ritual verses of the various Dusun/Kadazan communities in the Tuaran plains, just to the west of the mountain, and the foothills of the massif, mention of Mt. Kinabalu has been almost inevitable. The imposing summit became revered by many as a final abode for the spirits of their dead. Although now largely dispensed with, rites for the appeasement of spirits, involving the sacrifice of fowls and sometimes offerings of eggs and betel nut or other items, were required by local guides of some of the earlier visiting expeditions.

Some of the many interpretations of the rich folklore around Kinabalu have it that the mountain's name is derived from *kina balu* (a corruption of local words that mean "Chinese widow"), in allusion to the failure of legendary Chinese attempts to obtain a pearl guarded by a dragon atop the mountain, resulting in death— and widowed women. However, it is more likely perhaps that the Dusun word *nabalu* is a root, generally believed to mean "resting place of the dead" or "a big boulder associated with spirits".

Kinabalu from the south.
About 93% of Kinabalu Park is covered with natural vegetation. The "tree line", above which forests do not develop because of ground frost and a lack of soil, is variable between 3350 m and 3700 m, occasionally transgressed by pockets of forest that survive in the shelter of soil-filled gullies.

Whatever the origin of the name, the origin of the mountain itself is somewhat more accessible to scientific interpretation. Geologists reveal the story begins some 40 million years ago, when the northwestern area of Sabah was still part of a sea basin, in which marine sediments were accumulating and forming layers over the earth's crust. The crust has

C. Clarke

zones of weakness in which new material from below came up, and other zones along where one margin is forced down below the other. The movement of such crustal segments, or plates, in this region created intense heat and the melting of rocks forced down below another plate margin. At the same time, molten granitic material was pushed upward along adjacent zones of weakness, in the Crocker Range area of present-day Sabah, and buckling and faulting of the thick sedimentary layers created the Crocker Range and Trus Madi highlands.

This granitic mass began consolidating to form the huge body known as the Kinabalu batholith, which up to about 10 million years ago was still not exposed. Radiometric dating suggests that the Kinabalu magmatic body cooled from 9 million to 4 million years ago, and it is said to be still pushing up at about 5 mm each year. It is thought that during the Pleistocene period some 100,000 years ago, the mountain was probably several hundred metres higher than today, so that an ice-cap crowned the summit, and that by this time much of the sedimentary rock cover at the top had been eroded, exposing the granite. There was certainly glaciation at the upper parts of Kinabalu, when huge chunks of ice formed and moved downslope, particularly promoted by alternate warmer and cooler climatic episodes then. The polished rock surface, the U-shaped gullies that trace the movement of glaciers at the summit region and its slopes, particularly on the western part, and the moraines (rock debris) left at the end of such gullies, are all signs of colder times. Even Low's Gully, the great 1800-m deep chasm to the north that separates the higher western summit plateau from the eastern plateau, once contained the main valley glacier. The summit ice cover disappeared about 3000 years ago.

EARTH, WIND, SUN AND MIST
Kinabalu's Environment and Natural Communities

T he Kinabalu massif, at the northern end of the Crocker Range and larger than the Park itself, is an important water catchment and source to many streams and rivers, including some of the most significant in Sabah. In the northern part, the Kinarom river feeds the Bongon that flows into the Marudu Bay, where also the Tuaran river empties. The Penataran and Kilambuan are just two of the larger streams that derive from the northwestern slopes, joining the Kedamaian which drains into the South China Sea. From the massif's southern limits, the Pegalan river issues generally southward and along the Tambunan valley, joining the Padas that finally enters the Brunei Bay. The streams that flow eastward from the Kinabalu area include the Bambangan, Mesilau and Liwagu, the last of which later meets the Labuk and empties into the Labuk Bay. There are also the Langanan, Nalumad and Kinapassan rivers on the eastern side, which connect with the Sugut that goes out to the Sulu Sea. These streams continue to carve up the rugged landscape of the area, providing many habitats for plants and animals, and play an important role in maintaining the characteristic hydrological balance of the places they run through.

At the same time that it is a primary factor which helps sustain such a vast drainage pattern, the elevation brings different parts of the Kinabalu massif to different climatic zones, as has been shown with some detail through the studies of ecologist Kanehiro Kitayama. On the average, there is a fall in mean temperature of around 0.55°C per 100 m increase in elevation, and the daily temperature difference also diminishes with altitude. Thus, in the lowland forests around the base of the mountain (and included in the western, northern and northeastern periphery of the Kinabalu Park), lowland climates with mean daily temperatures of around 28°C contrast with that in the summit region, where means dip to

9

(Right) From around 1200 m up to 2000–2350 m, Lower Montane Forest develops.

In this forest type, species of oaks (Fagaceae), conifers (especially *Dacrycarpus* and *Phyllocladus*) and the myrtle (Myrtaceae) and tea (Theaceae) families are among the most common, the trees reaching 25–30 m tall.

W.M. Poon

(Above) Mixed Dipterocarp Forest in the lowlands near Poring.

This rich forest type covers some 35% of Kinabalu Park. The trees reach 30–50 m tall and include at least 40 species of dipterocarps, a tree family that is dominant in the lowlands but which becomes rarer and is finally absent at higher elevations.

C. Clarke

around 6–8°C and on rare occasions there are freezing ground temperatures associated with drought. The lower temperatures and generally higher rainfall experienced upslope results in lower evaporation rates, higher air humidity and increasing water surplus and saturation of the soil, features characteristic of tropical mountains. On Kinabalu, the cloud zone that daily envelops the mid-slope region from 1200–2000 m to 3000–3200 m is a significant feature, bringing into the system a dramatic increase in moisture through condensation on the vegetation (a process which some ecologists have called "fog-stripping").

This does not mean that conditions remain invariable. Prolonged dry spells, in relation to El Niño Southern Oscillation events or other phenomena, have been observed by various workers during 1977, 1979, 1983 and 1992, and could be commonplace periodic events previously unnoticed.

The uniqueness of Kinabalu stems also from the development of a rich spectrum of vegetation on a variety of soils in relation to the occurrence of various rock types on the mountain and the altitudinal climates over its large elevational range. Kitayama confirmed that, roughly corresponding with altitude, four broad floristic zones develop: a lowland forest zone up to around 1200 m, a lower montane zone above this until about 2000–2350 m, then an upper montane zone up to about 2600–2800 m, and a subalpine zone distinct at 2800–3400 m. The boundaries of these zones represent "critical altitudes" where plant composition changes and species typical of one zone are replaced by those of another, and where distinct substrate and climatic characteristics develop.

For instance, above about 1200 m, distinct humic horizons (of highly decomposed organic material) develop in the soil, and mid-slope soils between 1200 and 2600 m have a higher organic carbon content and water-holding capacity. Soil peatiness develops as the montane forest begins, probably in response to reduced rates of organic matter decomposition with lower temperatures and lowered oxygen levels induced by soil saturation. The temperature regimes on Kinabalu correspond to a general tropical-type climate below 1200 m, a temperate-type climate above this to about 3610 m, and a polar-type

12

Trees in the Lower Montane Forest are generally smaller that those in the Mixed Dipterocarp Forest lower down, and peat begins to develop on the ground.

Upper Montane Forest, with an increased "mossiness" and a commonness of crooked, gnarled trees to only about 20 m high, develops above the lower montane zone, up to 2800–3000 m.

The montane forests of both upper and lower zones are well-irrigated by the daily cloud cover and together occupy about 37% of the Kinabalu Park area.

climate at the summit zone. The "ground frost" line at around 3700 m, which marks the limit below which ground freezing temperatures do not occur, also corresponds with the "tree line" (the upper limits of the subalpine woods), above which are only scrub patches scattered over an alpine rock-desert. The mid-slope cloud cover also results in physiological stress to plants through a high water surplus and reduced levels of transpiration and photosynthetically important radiation, and possibly even suppressed nitrogen uptake by plant roots.

Superposed on this general setting is a myriad of site conditions—such as plateaus or gentler slopes versus steeper slopes or cliffs, more sheltered habitats in valleys compared to exposed ridges, varying soil cover ranging to bare rock, and sites with different aspect (whether north- or south-facing, etc.)—and mosaics of soil derived from

14

(Left) Vegetation at the Panar Laban rockface, *c.* 3350 m elevation.

Subalpine forest, developing in places between about 3000 m and 3700 m, fills some gullies here, while elsewhere on the exposed summit granite an alpine rock-desert community of sparse, low plants is typical.

C. Clarke

(Right) Graminoid or grassland-type vegetation is found on the flatter, boggy parts on Marai Parai, the ultramafic western spur of Kinabalu, and grades into montane forest on the slopes.

K.M. Wong

15

ultramafic rocks which contrast with that developing from sandstones that form the main surface of Kinabalu and the granitic summit area. Ultramafic rocks, mainly serpentinites and peridotites, represent consolidated oceanic crustal material that had intruded the sedimentary rock layers in relation to past crustal plate movements in the region. They are made up of mostly mafic (dark) minerals, and are poor in potassium and phosphorus but rich in ferro-magnesium and nickel- and chromium-containing minerals. High levels of these elements are typically toxic to many plants. Recent work by Kitayama's group also demonstrates that the influences of temperature and moisture on rates of mineralisation and nitrogen availability to plants may differ significantly between soils developed from ultramafic and sedimentary rocks on Kinabalu.

Ultramafic rocks are found around the distinct peak called Mt Tambuyukon (2579 m) to the northeast of Mt Kinabalu, and also occur on Kinabalu itself on the western Marai Parai spur and the northwestern part, the upper Pinosuk plateau to the southeast, and as smaller isolates between 2700 and 3000 m on the southern and southeastern faces of the mountain. Several distinct communities, dominated by the trees *Tristaniopsis elliptica, Leptospermum flavescens, L. recurvum, Gymnostoma sumatranum* or a mixture of these with other species, are dispersed over such ultramafic substrates. In addition, graminoid (grassland-type) communities, dominated by sedges, also occur on Marai Parai and the summit of Tambuyukon. Over the granitic summit region, a range of alpine scrub communities develop, including heath-type shrub communities.

Low scrub-like vegetation on thin soils at *c.* 2250 m, dominated by grass-like *Machaerina* sedges and dwarfed *Leptospermum* trees, among which are some killed by the severe drought of 1983.

K.M. Wong

16

K.M. Wong

Gnarled and crooked, *Leptospermum recurvum* trees commonly dominate patches of soil developing on ultramafic rocks between 2200 m and *c.* 3000 m on the south face of Kinabalu.

In places, forests of 7–15 m tall develop on ultramafic soil and are variously dominated by *Leptospermum*, *Tristaniopsis*, *Dacrydium*, *Gymnostoma* and other trees. Vegetation on ultramafic soils is estimated to cover some 16% of Kinabalu Park.

The coral-like, many-branched fruit-body of *Clavicorona turgida*.
This species belongs to the Hericiaceae, which, like the Clavariaceae, are commonly
referred to as coral fungi. *Clavicorona* is a widespread genus of about a dozen species,
and the species mostly occur on damp rotting twigs, leaves and other debris.

A BEACON OF BIODIVERSITY
Plant Diversity and Speciation

Whereas the lowland forests have the highest number (i.e., greatest diversity) of tree species, the montane and subalpine forests, alpine scrub communities and vegetation facies on ultramafic substrate are incredibly rich in endemic species, i.e., those unique to these sites and not occurring elsewhere. Among ferns and fern-allies, 50 of the 611 species (8%) documented for Kinabalu by botanists Parris, Beaman & Beaman are endemic. Almost half of some 1500 species of orchids catalogued by Wood & Cribb for Borneo occur on Kinabalu, where slightly over 10% of its species are endemic. In the predominantly shrub and epiphyte genus *Medinilla*, 17 of the 48 species enumerated by Regalado for Borneo are found on this mountain (including seven endemic to it and the Crocker Range). Many endemic species of other plants, including *Rhododendron*, *Nepenthes*, oaks, conifers, bamboos and herbs, are known on Kinabalu alone, or just Kinabalu and the nearby Tambuyukon. Many such endemics are restricted to ultramafic sites, such as the pitcher plants *Nepenthes burbidgeae*, *N. edwardsiana*, *N. rajah* and *N. villosa*, the orchids *Dendrobium spectatissisimum* and *Paphiopedilum rothschildianum*, *Rhododendron meijeri* and *R. baconi* and the conifer *Dacrydium gibbsiae*.

The overall plant diversity of Kinabalu is staggering. Of some 650 species of mosses known in Borneo, more than half are found on Kinabalu. Beaman & Beaman estimate some 4000 vascular plant species occur on Kinabalu alone, which may be as much as 10% of that of the entire Malesian region, an intensely species-rich floristic region where Sumatra, the Malay Peninsula, Borneo, the Philippines, Java, Sulawesi, Maluku and New Guinea are the principal territories, and where biological inventories are in general extremely fragmentary. Many of

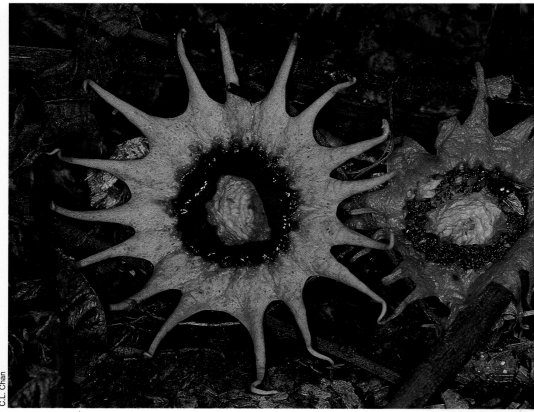

C.L. Chan

(Above) *Aseroë rubra*, the Red Rayed Stinkhorn.

The Stinkhorns are a group of fungi that assume many unusual forms in their fruit-body, where the spores are produced. In *Aseroë*, a genus of two species (both known in Borneo), the fruit-body consists of a short stalk surmounted by a disk bearing the gleba (the inner fertile or spore-bearing part). In *A. rubra*, the disk margin bears 14–22 bright-red cylindrical arms or rays which spread outwards at maturity. The ripe gleba undergoes autodigestion, producing a foul-smelling gelatinous substance that envelops the spores. Bluebottle flies attracted by the smell and red coloration, which mimic rotting red meat, visit the fungus to feed. In so doing, they carry away spores that stick to the fly, effecting dispersal of the fungus. This stinkhorn is widespread, occurring from Japan, Vietnam through southeast Asia, to New Guinea, Australia, New Zealand, Hawaii, central and south America, India, Sri Lanka, Tanzania and South Africa. In Borneo and other nearby islands, they appear to be common only in some montane areas, such as around the Kinabalu Park headquarters.

C.L. Chan

C.L. Chan

The pink-capped *Marasmiellus salmonicolor* (above) and the yellow *Xeromphalina tenuipes* (left) are but two of the many agaric mushrooms found on Kinabalu.

They belong to the Tricholomataceae family in the large order Agaricales, where a number of species have been shown to form mycorrhizal associations with the roots of trees. The resultant structure formed by the fungus and the root is called a mycorrhiza, a symbiotic arrangement where the fungus enhances the root's nutrient uptake from the soil and derives some water and food substances from the root tissue. *M. salmonicolor* frequently occurs on old tree bark, and *X. tenuipes* occurs on rotting logs. The little mushroom next to *X. tenuipes* is *Filoboletus manipularis*, of a different family and order.

Lichens, those composite organisms that are a partnership between a fungus and one or more algae, assume a variety of forms.

Thin, plate-like or ribbon-like foliose lichens (below) are common on tree trunks in the montane forests. In contrast (right), the *Usnea* (Old Man's Beard) lichens resemble tangles of string on the branches of trees and shrubs and are common in the upper montane and alpine vegetation on Kinabalu. The fungal tissues protect the alga from the intense sunlight and also absorb water and mineral elements, whereas the green-pigmented alga performs photosynthesis and provides the carbohydrates required for growth.

W.M. Poon

C.L. Chan

these plant species are extremely rare and poorly known, and the Beamans record some 40% documented from just a single locality, and about a third scientifically collected just once, on the mountain.

The extreme plant diversity on Kinabalu is supported by the rich variety of habitats on the massif due to elevation, climate, soil diversity and a rugged physiography, as well as the location of the mountain within the generally rich floristic region of Malesia. The comparative geological youthfulness of this mountain implies that it would have received plant species early on from other pre-existing communities, such as on the geologically older main Crocker range, and indeed exchange of species' propagules between Kinabalu and other places can still be expected to occur. But several other factors probably continue to fuel population and species differentiation, and consequently high evolutionary rates on the mountain, producing the neo-endemic species of restricted distribution (compare this with paleo-endemics, which are more ancient entities presently localised because of extinction throughout much of its original, wider range). The youthful physiography with sharp high ridges, and the occurrence of separate patches of special geology or vegetation communities on the Kinabalu massif could be effective in the isolation of populations and their specific genetic characteristics dispersed between sites.

Genetically variant populations may be maintained when they differ in their utilisation of a resource (e.g., when they are adapted to different soil or light conditions) in the complex heterogenous environment of an ecosystem, i.e., they do not compete directly. Disturbance factors which create habitat heterogeneity can help maintain such variant populations within a site. The occurrence of occasional, prolonged dry spells on Kinabalu may be such a factor, and the mortality of plant populations during drought events has also been noticed. Ecologist Kitayama has also suggested that such drought events that bring on water stress to plants on mountains may have increased the selection pressure for small and tough leaves, characteristic of many montane plant species. The depression of vegetation zones that probably occurred on Kinabalu in times of cooler temperatures during the Pleistocene Ice Ages also probably caused habitat conditions and extents to change and both extinction and selection of forms.

C.L. Chan

(Right) *Marchantia streimannii*.
Forming small, pure mats over damp ground, this liverwort has a thalloid plant body—one that is ribbon-like, undifferentiated into stem and leaves—which repeatedly forks. The minute cup-like structures on the upper side of the thallus contain the gemmae or vegetative bodies that sprout new plants, a mode of multiplication in addition to sexual reproduction.

(Left) The tiny, stalked red-headed fruit-bodies of a *Cladonia* lichen.
This lichen commonly colonises patches of exposed, severely weathered earth-banks in the upper montane zone.

C.L. Chan

C.L. Chan

(Above and right) *Selaginella* and *Lycopodium* are among the fern-allies found on Kinabalu.
The selaginellas (Selaginellaceae) on the mountain are typically low-creeping or suberect, rather delicate small plants in moist, shaded habitats, and some 14 species are known from Kinabalu. The club-mosses or Lycopodiaceae (also 14 species on Kinabalu) are represented by such interesting forms as *Lycopodium casuarinoides* (right), which can be an impressive climber to several metres high in lower montane forest at 1500–2700 m.

K.M. Wong

C.L. Chan

Dawsonia longifolia, a Giant Moss.

Turves of this moss, growing as high as a metre, are common in the montane forest up to about 2200 m and are easily spotted along trailsides on Kinabalu. The Giant Mosses (Dawsoniaceae) are confined to southeast Asia and there are two species in Kinabalu Park. *D. longifolia* ranges from New Zealand, Tasmania, east Australia, to New Guinea, Sulawesi, Borneo and the Philippines. *Dawsonia* leaves have tiny microfolds on their upper or ventral surface that hold superficial moisture and fold inwards when the air around dries out, protecting these water-storing leaf surfaces. The spore capsule of a *Dawsonia* moss (left) is borne on the female plant and contains tens of millions of spores that eject in puffs when the capsule is shaken by wind or raindrops.

K.M. Wong

Segregation of populations can also occur when variant forms that have arisen are very similar to existing ones in their resource demands and so compete, resulting in the range of one being diminished until both are spatially segregated. The occurrence of altitudinally segregated species of the same genus on Kinabalu may have had this origin in some cases. *Racemobambos hepburnii* (well developed at 1100–2200 m, and also found on the Crocker range) and *R. gibbsiae* (2000–3000 m, endemic to Kinabalu) are closely related bamboos that show such altitudinal segregation. Among *Machaerina* sedges on Kinabalu, the more widespread *M. disticha* and *M. glomerata* are common from the lowlands to about 1500 m, while *M. falcata* occurs at 1900–3300 m and the endemic *M. aspericaulis* is well developed at around 1500–1650 m. In addition to *Scaevola micrantha*, a tree endemic to ultramafic soils throughout Sabah, including in the lowlands, there are two other "ultramafic endemics" of this genus in the Kinabalu area: *S. verticillata*,

A. Lamb

C.L. Chan

(Left) Filmy ferns are abundant in and above the cloud zone on Kinabalu.

Filmy ferns (family Hymenophyllaceae) have extremely thin leaf-blades 1–few-cells thick, through which moisture is absorbed. These ferns are restricted to damp environments and are very vulnerable to drying out. The severe drought of 1983 was noticed to have completely extirpated some filmy fern species that were previously abundant in some habitats on Kinabalu. The Hymenophyllaceae are represented on Kinabalu by 16 genera with 56 known species.

(Above) *Sticherus hirtus*, a mountain *resam* fern. This species belongs to the Gleicheniaceae, a family of ferns known in the region by the Malay name *resam*. Kinabalu has four genera and 15 species of *resam*, of which only one appears to be endemic there. Repeated forking in *resam* leaves, which have indefinite growth in length, allows the species to form thickets where they occur. *S. hirtus* occurs in montane forest at 1200–2900 m on Kinabalu.

(Far left and left). Kinabalu Park's ferns and fern-allies include 611 species, about 5% of the world's. This unusual diversity includes both widespread, common and some rare forms. *Dipteris conjugata* (far left), also occurring in Peninsular Malaysia, Sumatra and the Philippines, is a common terrestrial fern of exposed sites such as trail sides and ridges. Among other characteristics, the netted veins of *Dipteris* leaves suggest a close relationship with *Cheiropleuria bicuspis* (left), another widespread montane fern also found on Kinabalu.

T.J. Barkman

Tree-ferns.

The trunked habit and large, dissected leaves of tree-ferns make them distinctive as a group. On Kinabalu, 22 species of *Cyathea* tree-ferns and *Dicksonia mollis*, a tree-fern known only in Borneo and the Philippines, have been recorded. Of the *Cyathea* species, six are endemic to Kinabalu, i.e., not occurring elsewhere. Some others, like *C. contaminans*, abundant around the lower montane forest area near Kinabalu Park headquarters, are common.

restricted to Mt. Tambuyukon, and *S. chanii*, known only from one population around 2000–3000 m on the south face of Kinabalu itself.

The common occurrence of many species of the same plant genus on Kinabalu, many of which are localised or rare, may have been contributed by such pathways of evolution, at least in part. Thus, for Kinabalu, Beaman & Beaman record 73 plant genera represented by 10 or more species, of which 30 genera have 20 or more species. The largest are *Ficus* (the genus of the figs, 98 species), the orchid-genus *Bulbophyllum* (88 species), the *kelat* or *ubah* genus *Syzygium* (at least 66 species), the orchid-genus *Dendrobium* (62 species), and the oak-genus *Lithocarpus* (46 species).

Kinabalu's high elevation has also allowed the existence there of plants of temperate or high-montane affinity, as has been discussed by the eminent botanist E.J.H. Corner, who led the Royal Society Expeditions to Kinabalu in 1961 and 1964, in a prelude to the gazettement of the Park. These include the dwarf-shrub *Drapetes ericoides* (known otherwise from New Guinea mountains), the trees *Photinia davidiana* and *P. prunifolia* (elsewhere known only from China, Vietnam and Sumatra) and the herbaceous *Potentilla parvula* (also on some high Philippine, Sulawesi and New Guinea mountains) and *Trachymene saniculifolia* (otherwise known only in Mindoro in the Philippines and eastern New Guinea). The conifers *Agathis* (3 species on Kinabalu) and *Dacrydium* (5 species on Kinabalu) are genera of Australasian affinity. In addition, temperate herb genera such as the eyebright (*Euphrasia*) and buttercup (*Ranunculus*) have representative species (*E. borneensis* and *R. lowii*) that are endemic to Kinabalu. There are also other, more widespread species of plants that range from afar, such as *Sanicula europea* (Europe and temperate Asia), *Nertera granadensis* (central and south America, south Australia, Polynesia, south China, Madagascar), and *Clematis smilacifolia* (Nepal to New Guinea).

Corner summed up accurately when he wrote that "Kinabalu is a scenic wonder, a test for mountaineers from the amateur to the skilled rock-climber, a holiday from the hot lowlands, and botanically a paradise." Kinabalu has also been described as a "beacon of biodiversity that looms over Borneo" and is truly one of the world's most important biological sites.

C.L. Chan

C.L. Chan

C.L. Chan

C.L. Chan

More than 30 species of gingers occur in Kinabalu Park, especially around the Poring Hot Spring area and up to *c.* 2000 m.

(Opposite page, top) *Alpinia havilandii*, endemic to Kinabalu and the mountains of west Sabah and Sarawak, is common around Park headquarters.

(Opposite page, bottom) Endemic to Mt. Kinabalu, *Amomum kinabaluensis* has heads of yellow flowers embedded in the forest-floor litter.

(Above, left) *Hedychium cylindricum* is an epiphytic ginger found in Sumatra, Java and Borneo. When ripe, the yellow fruit capsules split, revealing the bright red seeds.

(Above, right) *Burbidgea schizocheila*, usually less than a metre high, is one of 5–6 species of a genus entirely restricted to Borneo.

31

C.L. Chan

T.J. Barkman

(Opposite page) Rothschild's Slipper Orchid.

Its few known populations on Kinabalu extremely vulnerable to decimation by plant-thieves and catastrophes (such as fire, which has ravaged one population), *Paphiopedilum rothschildianum* commands much commercial interest and is also known as "Kinabalu Gold". Five of the 12 species of slipper orchids in Borneo occur on Kinabalu. The bent staminode of the flower is covered with glandular hairs, which are thought to mimic aphid colonies that are the natural brood sites for the syrphid fly *Dideopsis aegrota*. The deceived visitor falls into the slippery shoe-like lip of the flower and attempts escape by climbing up the hairs. It passes under the stigma and anthers, and is dusted with pollen which it carries to the next flower, there effecting pollination.

(Below) *Coelogyne hirtella*, one of about 40 species of necklace orchids on Kinabalu, occurs only in the mountains of Borneo.

This species is a low epiphyte in mossy forest at 1150–2350 m on Kinabalu.

W.M. Poon

33

(Right) A conspicuous orchid found only in the upper montane forest on Mt. Kinabalu, *Coelogyne papillosa* is not known to occur below *c.* 2500 m.

C.L. Chan

C.L. Chan

(Above) *Dendrobium lamrianum* is one of the rare orchids known from only a few specimens documented around the Park headquarters area.

(Right) This *Dendrobium, D. spectatissisimum,* is the only species of the genus in Borneo with spectacular large, white flowers.

This orchid is so far known only from the ultramafic Marai Parai ridge of Mt. Kinabalu, and is frequently epiphytic on *Leptospermum* trees.

K.M. Wong

T.J. Barkman

C.L. Chan

The largest orchid genus in Borneo and on Mt. Kinabalu, *Bulbophyllum* may have as many as 16 of its 88 species on Kinabalu endemic to the mountain.

(Above) *Bulbophyllum montense*, with its delicate blooms, is endemic to Kinabalu, occurring in the lower and upper montane forests.

(Left) *Bulbophyllum lobbii*, a low epiphyte on small trees in montane forest and a common Kinabalu orchid.

This is a widespread species, found from India to Peninsular Malaysia, Sumatra, Java and Flores to Borneo and the Philippines.

(Above) Extremely rare, the orchid *Liparis aurantiorbiculata* is only known from a few localities on the Crocker Range. On Kinabalu, it has only been collected from the Pinosuk plateau on the south side, where its habitat no longer exists, and on the Penibukan ridge to the southwest. This rare species is also conserved in the Park's Mountain Garden.

(Right) Blooms of *Spathoglottis macrochilina*, a common terrestrial orchid around Park headquarters and along the first part of the trail to the summit.

C.L. Chan

(Above) *Nabaluia angustifolia*, one of only two known species of this orchid genus on Mt. Kinabalu.

The genus *Nabaluia* is not known outside Borneo, and *N. angustifolia* has been recorded on Kinabalu and the Crocker Range only.

C.L. Chan

Begonia kinabaluensis, an elegant herb endemic to Kinabalu.

This species is only known from a few localities, including the Tohubang and Liwagu valleys, growing on riverbank rocks and damp places in forest shade. Just 30–40 cm high, the red hairy stems and leaf stalks and the glandular-hairy pink inflorescence bracts are distinctive of this species.

C. Clarke

(Left) *Nepenthes villosa*, endemic to ultramafic areas on Kinabalu. First collected by Hugh Low in 1858, this species is common at 2340–3240 m, typically epiphytic. There are about 30 species of pitcher plants in Borneo, half of which are found on Kinabalu.

(Left) *Nepenthes burbidgeae* is another pitcher plant endemic to the ultramafic areas on Mt. Kinabalu and Mt. Tambuyukon.

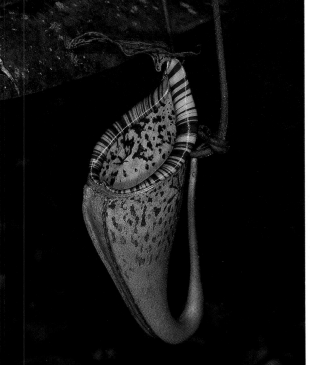

(Far left) *Nepenthes edwardsiana*. The coarsely corrugated red peristome that guards the mouth of the cylindric pitchers is characteristic. This species is found on both Mt. Kinabalu and the nearby Mt. Tambuyukon, occurring on both sandstone and ultramafic soils. It was first collected by Hugh Low.

(Opposite) The Rajah's Pitcher Plant.

Nepenthes rajah, endemic to ultramafic areas on both Mt. Kinabalu and Mt. Tambuyukon, was named for the Rajah James Brooke of 19th-century Sarawak. With probably the largest pitchers of any *Nepenthes* (pitcher capacity up to 3.5 litres), many types of small animals, especially insects, have been trapped in them. St. John records that Low even discovered a drowned rat in one of the pitchers.

C. Clarke

(Above) Low's Pitcher Plant (*Nepenthes lowii*), first collected by him in 1851.

Common at 1800–2400 m on Kinabalu and also found in montane forest elsewhere in Borneo, this species is distinctive by the narrow "waist" on the pitcher and the bristly lower side of its lid.

C. Clarke

Often nestled in wet moss or liverwort sods, the small pitchers of *Nepenthes tentaculata* are distinctive by the tentacular bristles on the lids.

The species is common throughout Borneo and is also found in Sulawesi. It is common on mossy mounds and slopes between 1200 m and 3000 m in the mountains.

C.L. Chan

K.M. Wong

(Above) *Rhododendron brookeanum* var. *kinabaluense*, endemic to Kinabalu and the Crocker Range, has flowers ranging from pale orange to dark red.

The species is a Bornean endemic with several subspecies and varieties, and the flowers are visited (and probably pollinated) by birdwing butterflies. Kinabalu has about half of some 50 species of rhododendron found in Borneo.

(Left) *Rhododendron stenophyllum* subsp. *angustifolium* occurs at 1500–2400 m on Kinabalu.

Found on a number of mountains in Borneo, this rhododendron has been widely cultivated in America, Australia and Europe. On Kinabalu, it is common between 2200 m and 2400 m along the summit trail, usually flowering between September and April.

C.L. Chan

The Heather Rhododendron, another Kinabalu endemic.
Rhododendron ericoides occurs from *c.* 2450 m to around 4000 m. A small tree at lower elevations, it grows as a bush barely 30 cm high among boulders at upper elevations. The flowers are just over 1 cm long.

(Left) Blooms of *Rhododendron crassifolium*, a shade epiphyte found mostly at 1200–2200 m on Bornean mountains.

(Below) Conspicuous inflorescences of *Rhododendron suaveolens*, a species usually found as epiphytes in the ridges around Park headquarters. Although the flowers are typically white, a pink-coloured form is known from the Penataran area on Kinabalu.

C.L. Chan

C.L. Chan

C.L. Chan

(Left) Probably the most common rhododendron on Bornean mountains, *Rhododendron fallacinum* is easily seen on ridges from 1500 m to 2500 m on Kinabalu. It is mostly epiphytic but can also grow as a tree, and hybridises with other species. The flowers are visited by sunbirds.

K.M. Wong

(Right) Celery Pine, with seeds.

The Celery Pine (*Phyllocladus hypophyllus*) is distributed from New Zealand, Australia and New Guinea to Borneo and the Philippines. Probably the most primitive living conifer, fossils of the genus have also been found in south America and west Antarctica. In *Phyllocladus*, the flattened leaf-like green branchlets (phylloclades) take on the function of true leaves, which are absent or exist in very reduced form. The male (pollen) cones and seeds are found on separate trees.

A. Lamb

(Above) *Dacrydium gibbsiae*, a conifer endemic to Kinabalu, occurs on ultramafic soils between 1500 m and 3600 m.

K.M. Wong

(Left) *Falcatifolium falciforme*, a conifer distributed from Peninsular Malaysia to the Riau-Lingga islands and Borneo, occurs at mid-montane elevations.
Falcatifolium is a member of the Podocarpaceae, a family represented by five genera and 17 species on Kinabalu.

C.L. Chan

(Above) *Schima brevifolia*, one of two species of the genus in Borneo, and known only from a few mountains in Sabah.
The other species, *S. wallichii*, is widespread in the region and several of its subspecies are represented on Kinabalu.

(Right) Bright red figs of a geocarpic species, *Ficus uncinata*, common in the region and often growing on alluvial flats prone to flooding.

(Opposite page) Postar Miun, from a Dusun community living near Kinabalu, with strings of figs borne on another geocarpic fig, *Ficus treubii*.
Geocarpic fig species bear their figs on long runners issuing from the trunk base, but sometimes these runners also arise higher up. *F. treubii* is a common species at forest fringes and secondary forests near rivers at lower elevations on Kinabalu and elsewhere.

(Below and right) *Styphelia suaveolens*, a shrub or low tree with a heath-like habit. Although the species is distributed from the Philippines through Sulawesi and New Guinea to Australia and New Zealand, it is found in Borneo only on Kinabalu, occurring at 1800–4000 m and flowering throughout the year. Male and female flowers are produced on separate plants.

Blooms of *Clethra pachyphylla*, a tree found only in Sabah and northeast Sarawak and common in the lower montane forest on Kinabalu.

The Clethraceae are closely related to the Ericaceae, the rhododendron and heather family, and include *c.* 64 species, mainly in north and tropical America and Asia. Only three species of *Clethra* occur in Borneo.

(Left) Sweetly scented yellow flowers of *Wikstroemia tenuiramis*.

Wikstroemia is a genus ranging from southeast Asia to Australia and the Pacific, with six species in Borneo. *W. tenuiramis* occurs in Sumatra, Banka and Borneo, at lower montane elevations. It is said to produce wood that gives a fragrance when burned.

(Below) *Lithocarpus luteus*, an endemic Bornean oak common in Kinabalu's lower montane forests.

There are more oak species in tropical than in temperate areas, and the Indo-Malayan region alone has *c.* 300 species of *Lithocarpus*. Other genera of the oak family, such as *Castanopsis*, *Quercus* and *Trigonobalanus*, also occur on Kinabalu.

K.M. Wong

K.M. Wong

K.M. Wong

(Above) *Scaevola micrantha*, a relative of the Malayan rice-paper plant *S. sericea* which grows on southeast Asian and Pacific beaches, is endemic to Sabah's and the southern Philippines' ultramafic areas.

Three of the five species of *Scaevola* known in Borneo occur in Kinabalu Park, including *S. micrantha* (also known in lowland ultramafic areas elsewhere in Sabah), *S. verticillata* (endemic to ultramafic soils on Mt. Tambuyukon only) and *S. chanii* (known from only one ultramafic locality on the south side of Kinabalu). This kind of distribution illustrates the correspondence between genetic isolation, such as in ultramafic areas that are like habitat islands, and speciation or the evolution of new forms.

(Opposite page) *Scaevola chanii*, a bushy small tree in the upper montane forest on ultramafic soil at 2500–3000 m on Kinabalu.

Inset shows the smaller leaves with much shorter stalks and a little-branched inflorescence compared to those of *S. micrantha*, from which it is also distinguished in the details of the flowers.

(Right) Long shreds of bark fall away from a colourful and smooth trunk of *Tristaniopsis bilocularis* in the lower montane forest of Kinabalu.

Tristaniopsis, with *c.* 30 species, is distantly related to the eucalypts of Australia, which are not native to Borneo. These trees are known as *lumununu* in some Dusun dialects around Kinabalu.

(Above) *Leptospermum recurvum* is restricted to Kinabalu, generally occurring higher up than the related *L. flavescens*, which is a more common montane tree in the Sunda region.

L. recurvum varies from being a gnarled, twisted tree to a dwarf shrub on the rockfaces just below the Kinabalu summit. The typical form has smooth leaves, but a grey hairy form has been detected.

C.L. Chan

K.M. Wong

C.L. Chan

(Above) *Photinia davidiana* is a temperate East Asian element that occurs in the tropics only in subalpine forest and shrubland on the highest mountains of north Sumatra and on Mt. Kinabalu. The tree produces terminal panicles of red, berry-like fruits and occurs at much lower elevations in mainland Asia. A related species on Kinabalu with much the same distribution is *P. prunifolia*.

K.M. Wong

C.L. Chan

(Above) *Lobelia borneensis*, a common shrub in lower montane forest.
The Bornean lobelia occurs also in east Kalimantan and Sulawesi. The lobelias are a subtropical to tropical and mainly American genus classified as part of the Campanulaceae family. The flowers have variously coloured corollas, ranging from blue-purple to white with purple at the base of the corolla segments.

(Above) *Glochidion*, a tree genus in the rubber-tree family with some 40 species in Borneo, is represented on Marai Parai (the ultramafic western spur of Kinabalu) by several species, including this probably unnamed species.

(Right) Silver Potentilla.
This rare species, *Potentilla borneensis*, is known only from the high mountains of Sumatra and Mt. Kinabalu. Its closest relatives are a species in the Himalayas and Taiwan and another in Sulawesi and New Guinea. On Kinabalu it is found at 3500–4000 m, in the subalpine and alpine zones. *Potentilla* is a mainly north-temperate genus.

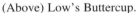

(Above) Low's Buttercup.
The 500 species of buttercup are mostly temperate plants, with 36 in the Malesian region. Low's Buttercup (*Ranunculus lowii*) is endemic to Kinabalu, found at 2750–3950 m in relatively open conditions and on moist deep soil pockets. The rosettes are barely 30 cm high and flower throughout the year. It appears most related to species in Sulawesi, Maluku, New Guinea and New Zealand.

Trachymene saniculifolia, the Red Sanicle.
Forming scattered small rosettes or cushions, this umbellifer is found on open ridges, in patches of scrub and in rock crevices, from about 2150 m to the summit area. Widely distributed from New South Wales through east New Guinea to the southern Philippines, this species is in Borneo known only from Kinabalu.

Trigonotis borneensis.
This herb is one of 35 species of a genus found in Asia and Melanesia, and is a Kinabalu endemic. The dense creeping mats with solitary white flowers produced in the leaf axils are distinctive, and are common in damp spots in the subalpine forest, scrub and alpine rock-desert community around the Laban Rata area on the mountain.

(Above) *Balanophora lowii*, a montane root-parasite.
All three species of the parasitic genus *Balanophora* on Kinabalu are not endemic there, but can be generally found in the mountains of Borneo. *B. lowii*, occurring in Sabah and Sarawak, has distinctive warted tubers that bear 6–8 pairs of apricot-pink leaves and either male or female inflorescences.

(Left) Sundews.
Like tiny glistening jewels, these sundews form rosettes, barely 2 cm across, of spatula-shaped leaves bearing elegant glandular hairs that are a sticky trap for unwary insects, which are broken down by the enzymatic fluids secreted. The species on Kinabalu is *Drosera spathulata*, one of two species documented for Borneo, and occurs in boggy sites in scrub and forest over ultramafic rock on this mountain.

(Right) Low's Blackberry.
A low, sparsely thorny straggly
climber of forest edges and
secondary forests, *Rubus lowii* is
endemic to Mt. Kinabalu, occurring
between 2750 m and 3950 m. It is
related to some species in Sulawesi
and New Guinea.

(Below) *Medinilla speciosa*.
This common shrub around the
Park headquarters is one of the 17
species known on the mountain, 48
species having been recorded for
the whole of Borneo.

(Left) *Phyllagathis elliptica*, a lower montane herb barely 30 cm high, produces pretty pink blooms that are a special delight along the trails around Park headquarters.

C.L. Chan

(Below) *Smilax* in fruit.
The genus of the wild sarsaparilla of eastern north America, *Smilax* is represented by a number of interesting species in Borneo and on Kinabalu. They are all tendrilled spiny climbers and produce their flowers and fruits in an umbel.

K.M. Wong

K.M. Wong

(Left) *Aletris foliolosa*.
This rather common stemless liliaceous herb at 2000–3450 m on Kinabalu grows in mossy forest or among the open scrub. The species is known only from some mountains in north Sumatra and on Mt. Kinabalu, but plants from these places show some minor differences which could represent some kind of evolutionary divergence.

K.M. Wong

Kobong-kobong.
This is the Dusun name for *Racemobambos hepburnii*, one of two extremely elegant, narrow-leafed bamboos on Kinabalu, common in lower montane forests between 1550 m and *c.* 2250 m and also found on other mountains in the Crocker Range. Baraham Buhari of the Forest Research Centre shows the pencil-thin culms or stems which can produce long whip-like branches that help form the thickets typical of this clambering species.

K.M. Wong

(Left) Miss Gibbs' Bamboo in gregarious flowering. *Racemobambos gibbsiae*, closely related to *R. hepburnii*, is restricted to Kinabalu's montane forests at its upper elevations. It also forms thickets which senesce and dry up after the characteristic grand displays of mass flowering. *R. gibbsiae* is known to have flowered in 1910, 1933, 1957, 1967 and 1979–81, but it appears that so far, none of these episodes have coincided with the flowering of the lower-elevation *R. hepburnii*. It is named after Lillian Gibbs, one of the first botanists to have studied plants on Kinabalu.

K.M. Wong

C.L. Chan

(Above) Young inflorescence of *Pinanga pilosa*.

Pinanga pilosa is a clumped palm hardly 1.5 m tall, common in the forest undergrowth around Park headquarters. There are 52 species of palms, in 10 genera, on Kinabalu, including only two endemics.

(Above) The largest of the mountain rattans, *Plectocomia elongata* thrives in large forest gaps, open ridge tops and old land-slips.

The cane (stem) is ensheathed in its characteristic spiny casing, and the large leaves, to 5 m or longer, bear its leaflets in groups. The whole massive cane dies after flowering takes place near the stem apex. The inflorescence branches are covered in large dark bracts that make them look superficially like large braids of hair, and parts of these are frequently encountered on the forest floor on ridges in the lower montane forest.

Alocasia cuprea.

Resembling medieval warriors' shields, the leaves of *Alocasia cuprea* are metallic green on the upper surface, and a deep maroon underneath. An equally impressive stalk of bright red fruits (above) is produced by mature plants. The species is a terrestrial aroid endemic to Borneo but has occasionally been cultivated as an ornamental houseplant. In the Kinabalu Park it can be found in the forests around Poring.

S.P. Lim

(Right) Securely attached to a leaf with its strong posterior sucker, a Tiger or Painted Leech (*Haemadipsa picta*) wavers about, waiting to detect the warmth of a passing mammalian animal.

This is the rarer of the two species of leech, both blood-sucking, most commonly encountered in Borneo's lowland forests, including those at the base of Kinabalu. Visitors to the Park headquarters and the upper parts of Kinabalu will seldom—if at all—see this leech.

C.L. Chan

C.L. Chan

(Left) Laden with its home, a discoid shell about 4 cm wide, *Rhinocochlis nasuta* goes about its nocturnal foray.

This snail is a widespread Bornean species but is only locally common around 1800 m on Kinabalu.

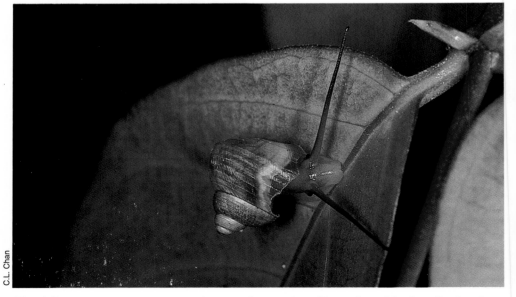

C.L. Chan

The delicate *Leptopoma sericatum* is one of more than 40 species of land snails found on Kinabalu.

Widely distributed in Borneo, this tiny snail, with its shell bearing fine spiral ribs, is known to occur around 1300 m on Mt. Kinabalu.

THE MOBILE RESIDENTS
Kinabalu's Animal Life

T he animal life makes up another fascinating aspect of Kinabalu, but is in general not very conspicuous to the untrained eye. The larger animals are shy, as can be expected. Even some of the "more accessible" birds to the earlier visitors, such as the Kinabalu Friendly Warbler (*Bradypterus accentor*, endemic to the upper slopes of Kinabalu, Tambuyukon and Trus Madi), are not as easily encountered along the trails, probably having moved to quieter areas. Intending animal watchers should, of course, move quietly and in small numbers. A number of groups are essentially nocturnal in habit, such as the Slow Loris and Tarsier, which foray on the trees at night, bats and a great many interesting invertebrate animals, including insects.

Some groups of animals, including land snails (most recently documented by Vermeulen) have distributions reminiscent of plants in general. More than half of the 43 known species of land snail on Kinabalu, especially those above 3000 m, are endemic there; three genera, *Gunongia*, *Kionghutania* and *Sabalimax* were first known from this mountain, and their few species there are all endemic.

Among at least 112 moth species on the mountain documented by Holloway, mostly Geometrid, Lymantrid and Noctuid moths, there is more than 50% endemism from about 2500 m to the summit zone, and a third of the lower montane species are so far known only from Kinabalu. Of the high-altitude moths, several species are shared with Sumatra, the Philippines, Sulawesi, Maluku and New Guinea, and there are also endemic Kinabalu representatives (e.g., *Diarsia barlowi* and *Hypocometa titanis*) of genera that are centred elsewhere (in west China and southeast Asia-Papuasia, respectively). The influence of isolation or past climatic changes on speciation (the evolution of new forms) on the mountain is also probably reflected by the presence of related pairs of

(Continued page 71)

65

(Right) Armed with its deadly sting, a *Scolopendra* centipede roams the night in search of prey.

Known as *tangkalamai* in the Dusun language, this centipede feeds on small insects, such as crickets.

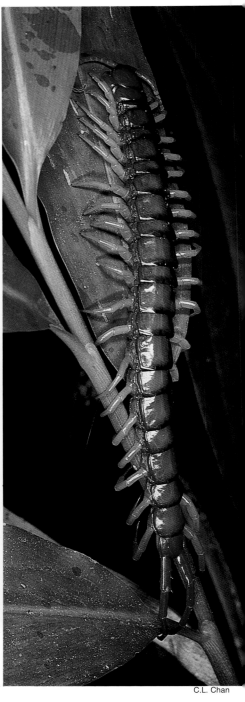

C.L. Chan

(Above) Long-legged centipede.

Elegant yet dangerous, *Scutigera* centipedes have distinctive long legs.

C.L. Chan

(Left) *Haaniella scabra*, a stick-insect endemic to Kinabalu.

This species is one of the few spiny stick-insects of Borneo. It displays an unusual defence behaviour in raising its abdomen and using its hind legs to squeeze the intruder. The genus *Haaniella* includes *H. echinata*, also spiny, which lays the largest eggs in the insect world.

(Below) *Lonchodes harmani* dangles from a leaf, looking like a dead twig.

About 15 cm long, this stick-insect drops to the forest floor at the first sign of danger, where among the dead leaves and twigs it is difficult to recognise.

(Right) Itself leaf-like, a *Deispona* longhorn grasshopper scours a leaf surface for tiny algae, on which it feeds. This unusual longhorn (tettigoniid) grasshopper can lie flat, mimicking a leaf. When disturbed, it lifts its back, kicks its hind legs and flutters its wings.

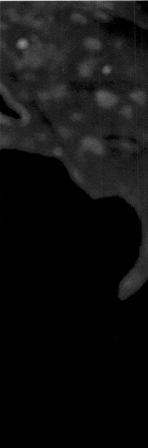

A.Y.C. Chung

(Above) A praying mantis, master of mimicry and deceit, lies in wait.

Toxodera denticulata, like other mantids, is predatory and eats other unwary insects that move too near to where it perches in lifeless stance. This rather rare insect is found in the lowland forest near Poring.

68

C.L. Chan

C.L. Chan

(Left) *Euphophyllum* sp., probably endemic to Mt. Kinabalu.

The tibia of its hind-legs are modified, looking like young *Macaranga* leaves complete with the marginal teeth. Such a form may be advantageous in avoiding potential predators as this tettigoniid grasshopper specialises in eating *Macaranga* leaves and spends much time on these trees.

(Above) A still chrysalis, from which will emerge the new adult of a Bluebottle butterfly (*Graphium sarpedon*).
The chrysalis, the pupal stage in the metamorphosis to an adult, is often made on a leaf that the caterpillar was feeding on. This swallowtail butterfly is common in southeast Asia and often congregates on riverbanks in search of the salts they require.

(Above) *Vindula erota*.
This nymphalid butterfly feeds on animal dung and rotting carcasses and is a fairly common species.

Brooke's Birdwing.
Another wide-ranging species found from lowland to lower montane forests, the females of this butterfly (*Trogonoptera brookiana*) are mostly found in the forest canopy and rarely descend to ground level.

moth species, such as *Agylla bisecta* (endemic to Kinabalu) and *A. divisa* (Borneo to the Himalayas), and *Hypocometa titanis* (endemic to Kinabalu) and *H. leptomita* (also in Sarawak).

Many other insects, including beetles, are diverse on Kinabalu and have adapted to very many different habits and diets. They show various patterns of distribution on the mountain, and many species remain undescribed or little known. Beetles and weevils represent probably the most diverse order in the animal kingdom, and include carnivores, herbivores (some wood-feeding), parasites and scavengers. They are richly represented on Kinabalu, with many species known only from there, and Chan, Ueda & Fatimah have surveyed the beetle diversity generally. Unusual and easily recognisable forms occur, such as among the fiddle beetles (*Mormolyce* spp.) whose bodies are flattened and shaped like violins, the stag beetles characterised by their kinked antennae (of which *Odontolabis femoralis* is commonly attracted to lights at Park Headquarters), and the rhinoceros beetles with their well-developed horns (the Two-horn Rhinoceros Beetle, *Xylotrupes gideon*, being most common). The trilobite beetles of the genus *Duliticola* have larvae resembling extinct, ancient trilobites, with black body segments with a bright orange-red edge, and their females retain this larval form into sexual maturity. Fantastic colours and patterns also decorate many groups, including ground beetles, ladybirds, longhorn beetles, leaf beetles, jewel beetles, tiger beetles and flower-chafers.

Beetles exhibit a varied range of biological phenomena common among insects, including camouflage (disguise through form or colour), mimicry (close resemblance in form or habit to some object or species), sexual dimorphism (different forms or sizes between the sexes) and specialised defensive behaviour. When threatened, bombardier beetles (with *Bruchinus bigutticeps* common around Poring) expel from their abdomens a foul-smelling hot fluid, making a bursting sound. Dung beetles scavenge and roll animal droppings into balls, which they bury in specially dug holes; the eggs are laid into the dung balls, which the larvae feed on when they hatch. Like beetles, stick-insects are also diverse in habit and form, and many interesting and rare species occur on Kinabalu, ranging from the spine-covered, clumsy and largely lowland *Haaniella echinata* to some slender uncommon species of *Lonchodes*.

Some of these insects, especially when they are common, feed on a wide range of plants, but a number are sometimes quite host-specific.

Among vertebrate forms, there are 40 fish species documented for the mountain and its surroundings by Chin, but none appear to occur above 1580 m. In the mountain streams, Gastromyzontid fishes (including four species of *Gastromyzon*, a genus of mostly bottom-dwelling sucker fishes endemic to Borneo) are the most common. Inger, Stuebing & Tan estimate some 75 species of frogs and toads for Kinabalu, most of which are lowland forest or lower montane forms. The slender toads (*Ansonia* spp.) and bush frogs (*Philautus* spp.) have representatives occupying different elevation intervals up to the subalpine zone, a number with overlapping distribution. The distribution of snakes and lizards reflects the same general trend, but perhaps more dramatically: the number of

(Right) A colony of *Euproctis* cocoons and their emerging adult moths.
This lymantriid moth is a common species of the sub-canopy level in lower montane forests at *c.* 1000–2000 m.

K.M. Wong

(Left) Oblivious to its environment, but hairy and vividly coloured enough to look dangerous to potential predators, a moth caterpillar crawls along on its feeding rounds.

C.L. Chan

(Above) The Giant Atlas Moth, *Attacus atlas*, "crowned" by its impressive pectinate (gill-like) antennae.

The largest moth in the world in terms of wing span (reaching 25 cm), this species occurs from the lowlands up to lower montane elevations throughout southeast Asia and the feeding of its larvae at times reaches outbreak proportions.

C.L. Chan

Trilobite beetle.

So called because their larvae resemble the ancient segmented trilobites now extinct, *Duliticola* beetles feed on rotten wood on the moist forest floor. The females retain the larval form even when they mature and move sluggishly about the ground.

C.L. Chan

(Above) Flower-chafer.
The flower-chafers, a subfamily (Cetoniinae) of
the large Scarabaeidae family, are the best fliers
among beetles. This metallic green species of
Pseudochalcothea, about 3 cm long, feeds on
nectar from flowers in the daytime. This group of
beetles is very speciose on Kinabalu and many of
these appear to be endemic there.

(Right) An extremely rare, nocturnally active
scarab beetle of the Rutelinae subfamily.

C.L. Chan

(Right) Three-horned Rhinoceros
Beetle.
Endemic to Borneo, *Chalcosoma
mollenkampi* displays marked sexual
dimorphism, common among beetles
of the dynastid subfamily: here the
male has well-developed horns and is
quite smooth on its back, whereas the
female has no horns and is covered
with short, rust-red hairs. The species
is commonly found attracted to lights
at the Park headquarters at night.

W.S. Fletcher

species attenuates with increasing altitude. For these cold-blooded animals, the cooler and cloudier climate of the upper elevations seems highly restrictive. Inger & Tan reveal that only about 20 species of snakes and lizards are known from about 1500 m (Park Headquarters) to 2200 m, the highest elevation where reptiles are known on Kinabalu; in contrast, at least 40 species are known in the lowland forests of Kinabalu Park. A few snakes, such as the King Cobra in the lowlands, or the triangular-headed pit-vipers, are poisonous and require more respect than usual.

The expeditions of the zoologist John Whitehead, who visited Kinabalu in 1887, 1888 and 1899, laid the foundations of knowledge about Kinabalu's bird life. Jenkins, de Silva, Wells & Phillipps have now catalogued 306 species of birds for the Kinabalu area (more than half of all bird species known for Borneo), of which 262 are resident, including 77 that can be considered montane specialists and 23 endemic to Borneo. Around Park Headquarters, a number of both rare and common birds can be expected: barbets, Blue-winged Leafbirds, bulbuls, Drongos, flowerpeckers and sunbirds, Kinabalu Serpent Eagle, Laughing-thrushes, Short-tailed Green Magpies, spiderhunters, Sunda Whistling Thrushes, tree-partridges and wood-partridges, Treepies, White-crowned Forktails, Whitehead's Broadbills, Whitehead's Trogon, woodpeckers and others. Some of these are rare, including the endangered Kinabalu

C.L. Chan

Pseudomyagrus waterhousei, a black-spotted blue longhorn beetle.
The "longhorns" have their antennae exceeding the body in length and include some of the most beautiful beetles in the world. *P. waterhousei* has been recorded from Sumatra, Peninsular Malaysia and Borneo, but is nowhere common.

C.L. Chan

Serpent Eagle (*Spilornis kinabaluensis*), known only from the higher mountains of northwest Borneo. Mt Kinabalu is also an important stop for migrant species, of which 27 have been documented.

According to Payne, the Kinabalu area has about a hundred species of primarily lowland mammals, of which about half the number are truly restricted to the lowland forest, the rest ranging beyond to the montane forest zones or even higher. For instance, the Red Leaf-monkey has been noted as high up as 3050 m, and Barking Deer and Sambar Deer have been recorded as high as 3350 m, in the subalpine zone. Of another 22 mainly montane species, more than half are endemic to Borneo, including the Black Shrew and Kinabalu Shrew, known only from Kinabalu. Kinabalu's mammals includes 22 species of bats, 26 squirrel species (probably more than any similar area elsewhere) and seven treeshrew species. Of the bats, there is the Large Flying-fox which is endowed with powerful flight and which has been observed at Poring, but a remarkable slender form is seen in the Greater Bamboo Bat, roosting in bamboo stems, which its enters and leaves through narrow slits hardly a centimeter wide. The squirrels range from the large Tufted Ground Squirrel, with a head and body length more than 30 cm and weighing more than a kilogram, to the tiny Pigmy squirrels less than 10 cm long and 30 g in weight. Kinabalu's most commonly seen mammal in the lower montane forest, including at Park Headquarters, is usually the Mountain Treeshrew, not known outside northwest Borneo.

There is also the Sun Bear, Clouded Leopard, Leopard Cat, civets, mouse-deer, porcupines, Pangolin, Slow Loris, Western Tarsier, Grey and Red Leaf-monkeys, Long-tailed and Pig-tailed Macaques, and Bornean Gibbon, among others. Most of these are lowland animals, so that for their conservation in the Kinabalu area the lowland forest communities to the west, north and east are of importance. In the Kinabalu area, orang-utans are known only from the northern and eastern parts, and their population may be ecologically distinct from those in the eastern Sabah lowlands.

Of special interest also is the Ferret-badger, distributed from Nepal to Indo-China and in Java, known in Borneo only from montane forest on

(Continued page 87)

(Opposite) A hairy *Hyllus* spider makes a meal out of a moth.
Armed with exceptionally good vision, this jumping spider (family Salticidae) patiently stalks its prey before leaping onto it. There are about 4400 species of jumping spiders, mostly in tropical regions of the world; these spiders typically do not spin webs for prey capture.

(Above) An occasional visitor, the
Rhinoceros Hornbill (*Buceros rhinoceros*)
is one of six hornbill species known in
Kinabalu Park.

The characteristic succession of roars from this
hornbill, called *sungang* in Dusun, is one of
the most well-known bird calls that resound
through the rain forests of Borneo. Hornbills
are important dispersers of fruit and are
completely dependent on the forest for their
survival.

(Right) Indigo Flycatcher.

A very tame bird often seen around the Park
headquarters, the Indigo Flycatcher (*Eumyias
indigo*) usually resides in montane forests
between 1500 m and 1800 m.

(Left) Little Cuckoo-dove.
Widespread in southeast Asia, the Little Cuckoo-
dove (*Macropygia ruficeps*) is a resident of
submontane forests throughout Borneo.

(Above) Common Green Magpie (*Cissa
chinensis*), a resident of hills in the
lowland zone but also found up to *c.*
1800 m on mountains.

(Left) Bounty in mouth, a
Malaysian Treepie
(*Dendrocitta occipitalis*)
ponders its move.

(Right) Its hearty whistling chorus a distinctive call around the Park headquarters at daybreak, the Chestnut-capped Laughing-thrush (*Garrulax mitratus*) is most common around the lower parts of Kinabalu.

(Below) Mountain Blackbird (*Turdus poliocephalus*).

Known in Borneo only on Mt. Kinabalu, Mt. Tambuyukon and Mt. Trus Madi, this bird is otherwise a wide-ranging species from the Sunda islands to Taiwan and Samoa and the Lord Howe Islands. Although in the west Pacific it lives near sea level, in Borneo it is a bird of the upper montane and subalpine zones; nevertheless, during the intense drought of 1983 Mountain Blackbirds were noted much lower down on Kinabalu, around the Park headquarters.

M. Strange

M. Strange

C.L. Chan

(Above) A warty beauty, the Cinnamon Frog (*Nyctixalus pictus*) is a tree frog that lays its eggs in water collected within tree hollows.

C.L. Chan

(Left) *Philautus* sp., a bush frog found on low vegetation at mid-montane elevations on Kinabalu.

Different species of bush frogs can look similar but most are easily distinguished by their calls.

C.L. Chan

(Above) Sharp-nosed Tree Frog (*Rhacophorus acutirostris*).

C.L. Chan

(Left) The Large-eyed Litter Frog (*Leptobrachium montanum*), well-camouflaged against the forest floor, is a common ground frog all over Borneo.

A bizarre combination of blotches and spots adorns the body of the Kinabalu Gecko, *Gonydactylus baluensis*.

W.M. Poon

(Above) Red-tailed Racer
(*Gonysoma oxycephalum*).
A common non-poisonous snake
of both primary and secondary
lowland forests in Sabah, this
species is known—perhaps
somewhat tongue-in-cheek—as
mansak punti (meaning "ripe
banana") to some Dusun people
around Kinabalu, because it is
sometimes eaten.

(Left) The Pangolin (*Manis
javanica*) or *bulukun* in the
Dusun language, a toothless,
scaly mammal that eats only
ants and termites.

K.M. Wong

A. Lamb

W.M. Poon

(Above) Slow Loris (*Nycticebus coucang*).
A nocturnal primate, the Slow Loris (*pogog* in Dusun) searches out fleshy fruits and small animals such as insects as food. On Kinabalu, it occurs in lowland and, sometimes, lower montane forests.

(Opposite) The *tondirukut* or Western Tarsier (*Tarsius bancanus*).
This strange primate occurs throughout Borneo, in the lowlands, and is also found in Sumatra and nearby islands. The Dusun name *tondirukut* is derived from the word *rinukut* which means an assortment of items or a medley, alluding to the tarsier's ears, eyes, feet and tail, which resemble those of a bat's, owl's, frog's and rat's, respectively.

Kinabalu and the Crocker Range. Bones of the Ferret-badger have been discovered in deposits 20,000 years old in the Niah Caves in the lowlands of Sarawak. This and the distribution of the animal suggests that it was once more widespread, but that its population and range in Borneo have diminished (or been caused to diminish) considerably in modern times until it remains only in some montane forests. Likewise, the remains of the Lesser Gymnure, a shrew-like insectivorous mammal common in the lowlands and hills from southwest China through southeast Asia, Peninsular Malaysia, Sumatra and Java, and now known in Borneo only from the highlands of west Sabah and north Sarawak, have been discovered in Niah in the lowlands. Many animal populations are unable to survive habitat disturbance or hunting pressure, and Kinabalu remains a safe haven for many species.

A. Lamb

(Above) Swift and slim, a Greater Bamboo Bat emerges through a small slit in the bamboo internode where it roosts.
The bat, *Tylonycteris robustula*, is called *teriadong* in Dusun and often makes its home in stems of the *poring* bamboo (*Gigantochloa levis*). It is insectivorous and occurs in the lowlands up to *c.* 1000 m.

(Opposite) A Colugo rests, clinging to a tree trunk.
This mammal (*Cynocephalus variegatus natunae*) glides from tree to tree with the assistance of a fold of skin that extends between the front and hind legs on each side of the body. It is usually more active at night, and feeds on leafy shoots and possibly bark and tree sap. It has been recorded in Kinabalu in the lowlands around Poring. The common name "Flying Lemur" is unfortunate as these animals do not fly, but glide, and they are not related to lemurs. The local Dusun name is *langah*.

W.M. Poon

A SPECIAL HERITAGE
Conserving Nature's Wonders

These distinct vegetation types and their associated plant and animal communities, with many rare and special forms, make up the unique assemblage of ecosystems on this wonderful mountain. The wisdom of adequate conservation is realised in part by the dedication of sufficiently large areas of the many different types of vegetation and habitats to reservation for perpetuity. The Kinabalu Park is an obvious case that illustrates this.

History reveals that several things can happen to the natural heritage of any area when special care is not taken. Rare and localised plants and animals can disappear with the modification of their natural environment. Extinctions in areas where little or no scientific inventory has taken place can pass unlamented when the natural vegetation is damaged or altered. The extinction of species can occur via other processes. Prolonged drought and drought-fuelled forest fires can cause patch extinction and localised plant and animal populations can vanish. Forest fragmentation, caused by leaving behind only patches of forest after transsection of the habitat by tracks and clearings, can also interfere with natural biological processes. Residual patches of individuals can retrograde genetically because gene exchange opportunities are restricted by the spatial separation of breeding individuals. They can also degrade because of the "edge effect"—a small patch experiences more

(Opposite) *Rafflesia pricei*, a root and stem parasite of *Tetrastigma* lianas in north and northwest Borneo, produces some of the most spectacular blooms of the plant kingdom.

Apart from the flowers, *Rafflesia* plants consist of only tissue strands within the lianas they parasitize. Borneo has seven species of this amazing genus. *R. pricei* flowers grow to *c.* 30 cm across, whereas those of the Sumatran *R. arnoldii* reach to almost a metre across. *R. pricei* is pollinated by bluebottle flies, presumably attracted to the strange coloration and the faint unpleasant smell of the flowers.

(Right) Kinabalu Eyebright.
Endemic to the mountain, this eyebright
(*Euphrasia borneensis*) is quite
commonly encountered around 2450 m to
the summit. The eyebrights are generally
a semiparasitic herb genus, with many
species known to parasitize the roots of
other herbs, although on Kinabalu this is
hard to verify. The Kinabalu species is
related to other species in Australia and
New Zealand.

(Below) *Sinna calospila*, boldly
marked with maroon, black and
yellow, is one of Kinabalu's very
many colourful noctuid moth species.

C.L. Chan

C.L. Chan

influence from the outside compared to a larger one which may
successfully conserve species that are able to survive only in its well-
sheltered environment.

Two basic, critical areas of investigation of the plant and animal life must
progress if we are to know more about our natural resources and how
best to conserve them in different situations. The inventory of species
and survey of habitats and distribution must be given further emphasis.
To achieve a first, good documentation takes years and the skills of a
broad spectrum of specialists. Good work from different groups of
scientists, as we have seen, is helping in this direction in the case of
Kinabalu. Second, long-term studies of population changes in forests
will reveal the comparative stability of forest communities through time.
The information is useful in assessing the effectiveness of small

conserved patches by providing some idea of the rates of extinction and recruitment of species. Likewise, the information can be instructive base-line data for comparison with similarly logged-over forests elsewhere, and can help suggest modifications for effective forest management in those situations. Again, the example of conserving a large area like Kinabalu, or the Danum Valley in the east coast Sabah lowlands, is invaluable, and from many angles we must continue to uphold the value of this.

Many of Kinabalu's rare plants have not been documented again for over half a century since they were first collected on the mountain. Some populations may have vanished from where they were first documented on the lower slopes outside the Park, where agriculture, human settlement and other landuse have replaced the original forests. Some others may be simply very rare and confined to places that are little visited now, so that consequently further observation of them has been scarce or non-existent.

So, Kinabalu Park—with its wonderful mountain, its education and tourism programmes, its Mountain Garden displaying rare and unique plant forms, and the continuing efforts to attract and support biodiversity research—must be valued as a fundamental aspect of our heritage and culture. As Tom Harrisson, one of the most accomplished students of Borneo, declared, Kinabalu should stand "as an inspiration not only to conservationists, climbers and naturalists but equally to all men and women of goodwill, up there to admire, enjoy and even (if you will) worship."

C.L. Chan

(Left) The diminutive Kinabalu Slender Toad (*Ansonia hanitschi*) is endemic to Mt. Kinabalu.
Found usually on rocks along streamsides around 1500 m, this species is one of seven species of *Ansonia* known on Kinabalu. The different species are found at various elevations from the lowlands to the summit zone.

ACKNOWLEDGEMENTS

Datuk Lamri Ali (Director of Sabah Parks), F.S.P. Liew (Deputy Director of Sabah Parks), Eric Wong (Kinabalu Park Warden), J. Nais (Kinabalu Park Ecologist) and their staff members Dolois Sumbin, Ansow Gunsalam, Patrick Gindai and Paul Yambun facilitated and assisted with visits to Kinabalu Park, which made the study of a wide range of aspects possible. Every trip we have made to the Park has been memorable.

The University of Malaya provided the opportunity for K.M. Wong to work on portions of the book. Dr K. Kitayama, A.Y.C. Chung and Dr L.G. Saw assisted with specialist literature and information used in the writing of this account. Postar Miun patiently educated us with his deep personal knowledge of various aspects of Kinabalu plants and animals. We have also enjoyed a number of interesting discussions with T.J. Barkman. The following kindly provided identifications of a number of species depicted in the photographs: A.Y.C. Chung (insects); Dr J. Dransfield (palms); Dr J. Holloway (moths); Dr R.F. Inger (amphibians and reptiles); Dr Su-See Lee (fungi); S.P. Lim (*Styphelia*); Dr D. Pegler (fungi); Dr K. Reide (tettigoniid grasshoppers); M. Sands (*Begonia*); M. Strange (birds); Rob Stuebing (reptiles) and J.B. Sugau (local names of bamboos). Many of the plant identifications were possible only through the facilities at the Forest Research Centre in Sandakan, and we thank the successive Heads of the Centre, Dr Y.F. Lee, Robert C. Ong and Anuar Haji Mohamad, and A. Berhaman, Joan Pereira, S.P. Lim, Leopold Madani and Imran Yunus for their kind support. During field work, Lideh Sobal, Baraham Buhari, Suin Gambukas, Postar Miun, Ubaldus Majawal, Kambira Loloh and Sulaiman Talib have been extremely helpful. In the production of the book itself, Jacky K.H. Chua provided assistance with computer techniques used in the layout.

Finally, it would not be complete to neglect special mention of the following who have generously allowed the use of some of their magnificent photographs in this book; Tengku D.Z. Adlin, Todd Barkman, Tommy Chang, Arthur Chung, Charles Clarke, Tony Lamb, Francis Liew, S.P. Lim, P.K. Loi, W.M. Poon and Morten Strange.

REFERENCES

Beaman, J.H. & R.S. Beaman (1990) Diversity and distribution patterns in the flora of Mount Kinabalu. In: P. Baas, K. Kalkman & R. Geesink (eds.), *The Plant Diversity of Malesia*, pp. 147–160. Kluwer Academic Publishers, Dordrecht.

Clarke, C.M. (1997) *Nepenthes of Borneo.* Natural History Publications (Borneo) Sdn. Bhd., Kota Kinabalu.

Corner, E.J.H. (1964) A discussion on the results of the Royal Society Expedition to North Borneo, 1961. *Proceedings of the Royal Society,* B, 161: 1–91.

Davison, G.W.H. (1992) *Birds of Mount Kinabalu, Borneo.* Natural History Publications (Borneo) Sdn. Bhd., Kota Kinabalu.

Fatimah Abang (1996) The elegant longhorns. *Borneo Magazine* 2(3): 8–15.

Hillyard, P. (1994) *The Book of the Spider.* Hutchinson, London.

Inger, R.F. & F.L. Tan (1996) *The Natural History of Amphibians and Reptiles in Sabah.* Natural History Publications (Borneo) Sdn. Bhd., Kota Kinabalu.

Kitayama, K. (1991) *Vegetation of Mount Kinabalu Park, Sabah, Malaysia. Map of physiognomically classified vegetation, scale 1:100,000.* East-West Centre, Hawaii.

Kitayama, K. (1992) An altitudinal transect study of the vegetation on Mount Kinabalu, Borneo. *Vegetatio* 102: 149–171.

Low, H. (1852) Notes of an ascent of the Mount Kina-Balow. *Journal of the Indian Archipelago* 6: 1–17.

Lowry, J.B., D.W. Lee & B.C. Stone (1973) Effects of drought on Mount Kinabalu. *Malayan Nature Journal* 26: 178–179.

Mohamed, H. (1995) Mosses of Sayap – Kinabalu Park, Sabah. In: Ghazally Ismail & Laily Din (eds.) *Sayap – Kinabalu Park Sabah*, pp. 105–122. Pelanduk Publications, Petaling Jaya, Malaysia.

Parris, B.S., R.S. Beaman & J.H. Beaman (1992) *The Plants of Mt. Kinabalu 1. Ferns and Fern Allies.* Royal Botanic Gardens, Kew.

Payne, J., C.M. Francis & K. Phillipps (1985) *A Field Guide to the Mammals of Borneo.* The Sabah Society with World Wildlife Fund Malaysia, Kuala Lumpur.

Phillipps, A. & A. Lamb (1996) *Pitcher-plants of Borneo.* Natural History Publications (Borneo) Sdn. Bhd., Kota Kinabalu.

Whitehead, J. (1893) *The Exploration of Kina Balu, North Borneo.* Gurney & Jackson, London.

Wong, K.M. & A. Phillipps (eds.) (1996) *Kinabalu—Summit of Borneo*, revised and expanded edition. Sabah Society, Kota Kinabalu. *[Including informative chapters by* Chan, Ueda & Fatimah *(beetles);* Chin *(fresh-water fishes);* Corner *(plant life);* Dransfield *(palms);* Harrisson *(uniqueness of Kinabalu);* Holloway *(butterflies and moths);* Inger, Stuebing & Tan *(frogs and toads);* Jenkins, de Silva, Wells & Phillipps *(birds);* Payne *(mammals);* Regis *(folklore);* Vermeulen *(land snails).]*

Wong, K.M., C.L. Chan & A. Phillipps (1988) The gregarious flowering of Miss Gibbs' bamboo (*Racemobambos gibbsiae*) and Hepburn's bamboo (*R. hepburnii*) on Mount Kinabalu, Sabah. *Sabah Society Journal* 8 (4): 466–474.

Wood, J.J., R.S. Beaman & J.H. Beaman (1993) *The Plants of Mount Kinabalu 2. Orchids.* Royal Botanic Gardens, Kew.

Wood, J.J. & P.J. Cribb (1994) *A Checklist of the Orchids of Borneo.* Royal Botanic Gardens, Kew.

The authors

A.S. Kamariah

Wong Mui Yun

K.M. Wong (left) is a botanist interested in the flora and natural history of Borneo and Peninsular Malaysia. Since 1980, he has lived and held assignments as forest botanist in Peninsular Malaysia, Brunei and Sabah, and is currently with the University of Malaya in Kuala Lumpur.

C.L. Chan is a naturalist with special interests in orchids and stick-insects. He is a collaborator on the Orchids of Borneo project organised between the Sabah Society, of which he is a long-serving member of the committee, and the Royal Botanic Gardens, Kew. He also works on the taxonomy of Bornean stick-insects together with other specialists.